Reading STREET

Grade 1

Scott Foresman

Decodable
Books 104-127
Unit 4

Scott Foresman
is an imprint of

Glenview, Illinois • Boston, Massachusetts • Mesa, Arizona
Shoreview, Minnesota • Upper Saddle River, New Jersey

Illustrated by: Dan Vick

ISBN-13: 978-0-328-37827-2
ISBN-10:   0-328-37827-5

1 2 3 4 5 6 7 8 9 10 V054 17 16 15 14 13 12 11 10 09 08

Contents

Tay on the Trail

Written by Susan Bloom

Decodable Book 104

"It's not raining," said Dad.
"We can hike on the trail."
Gail asked, "May we take Tay?"

1

They walked on the trail.
Tay left the main path.
Gail could see his tail.

"Don't stray, Tay," called Gail.
Tay barked.
Did he spy a snake?

No, it was a plain old snail.
"Wait, Tay!" called Gail.
Tay didn't stay.
He barked more.

Did Tay spot a skunk?
No, it was a jay.
"This way, Tay!" called Gail.
Tay still strayed.

Tay barked more.
Oh, my! What was it?
It was a gray cat.

Gail said, "Tay, you're a pain.
The trail isn't a place to play.
Next time you'll stay home!"

Long *a* Spelled *ai*

raining	trail	Gail
main	tail	plain
snail	wait	pain

Long *a* Spelled *ay*

may	Tay	stray(ed)
stay	jay	way
gray	play	

High-Frequency Words

said	the	they
could	a	was
old	oh	what
you're	to	you'll

A Day in May

Written by Chad Cox

It is a gray day in May.
This rain won't stop Ray.

"I will use this in the rain.
It will keep me dry!"

Ray has roses in his yard.
"Roses are just right for Gail,"
Ray thinks.
He picks red roses for Gail.

Gail is at home.
She broke her leg.
Ray takes the mail to Gail.

They play a game.
Gail is smart. She uses her brain.
She wins the game.

Ray brings Gail lunch on a tray.
"Does this make you smile?"
asks Ray.

Ray waves good-bye to Gail.
He takes the short way home.
Ray had a fine day.

Long *a* Spelled *ai*

rain	Gail
mail	brain

Long *a* Spelled *ay*

gray	day
May	Ray
play	tray
way	

High-Frequency Words

a	won't
the	right
to	they
does	you
good-bye	

My Family's Pets

Written by Helen Shay

Decodable
Book
106

My family's pets do
many funny things.
We can tell lots
of fun pet tales.

Have you ever seen a puppy sing?
Our big, black puppy Sam sings.
He can bark the notes.
Sam's songs go on and on.

Dan has twin cats.
Dan's cats run fast!
Muff and Puff zip
from place to place.

19

See the cats' bed.
Dan's cats like socks.
The cats play
with Dan's socks.

Liz's bird Bing is big and gray.
Bing likes to sit and talk.

Bing likes the mailman.
Bing tells him a silly joke.
Bing's joke makes the mailman smile.

Bing's joke is funny.
Sam's songs are funny.
The cats are quick.
They are funny pets.

Possessives

family's	Sam's
Dan's	cat's
Liz's	Bing's

High-Frequency Words

do	many
of	have
you	a
our	the
to	

24

Jay's Mail Day!

Written by Kelley South

When it rained one day in May,
Jay asked, "When will I get mail?"

Jay can see the mailman.
The mailman's bag looks big.

What will Jay's mail be?
Will it be a rain hat?
Will it be a small train?

Jay said "hi" to the mailman.
Some mail has Mom's name on it.
Jay takes the mail to Mom.

28

"Is that mail for me?" Jay asked.
"This note is for Jay," said Mom.

Mail for him!
Jay's mail makes him smile.
This is a happy day!

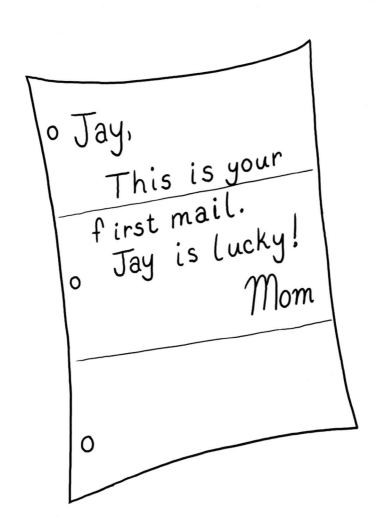

Word Lists

Possessives

mailman's
Jay's
Mom's

High-Frequency Words

one	the
looks	what
a	said
to	some
your	

Peaches and Cream

Written by Denise Ngo

Bea lives by a tree on a farm.
She eats meals of beans and peas.

In summer, ripe peaches gleam
on Bea's tree.
Bea leaps up, but she can't
reach them.

34

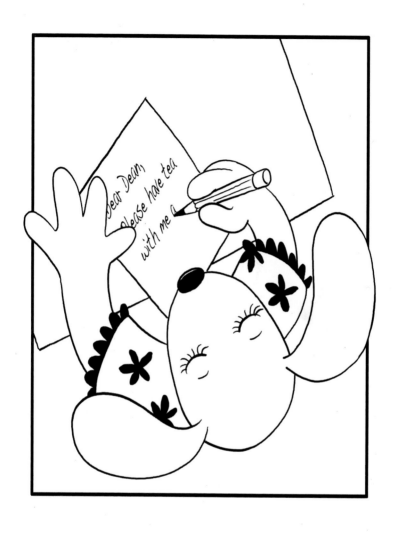

Bea sends a note to Dean.
"Dear Dean,
Please have tea with me
at my tree."

Bea asks, "Can you get the peaches?"
Dean's beak is sharp,
but not sharp enough.
The peaches stay on the tree.

When Daisy sneaks by,
Bea speaks to her.
"Can you get the peaches?"

Daisy gets up in the tree and
beats on the branch.
Peaches fall in a heap.
Bea beams.

38

Bea, Dean, and Daisy have
a feast.
Peaches and cream are
a real treat.

Long *e* Spelled *ea*

Bea	eats	meals
beans	peas	peaches
gleam	Bea's	leaps
reach	dear	Dean
please	tea	Dean's
beak	sneaks	speaks
beats	heap	beams
feast	cream	real
treat		

High-Frequency Words

lives	a	of
to	have	you
the	enough	are

40

Home by the Sea

Written by Alex Paloma

Decodable Book 109

We take a trip
to see friends.
Meg and Ted's home
is by the sea.

We do many things
with Meg and Ted.
We go to the beach.
We pick up shells.

Ted digs holes.
We plant bean seeds.
Ted and Meg teach us
about plants.

We ride bikes to the park.
Ted pushes us
on the swing.

44

Ted makes meals.
We eat meat and peas.
Meg grows huge peaches.
We eat them with cream.

We read together on the rug.
Ted tells us tales
about neat places.
Meg drinks a cup of tea.

When we say good-bye,
we are not happy.
We will send notes to Meg and Ted.
We had a fun time.

Long e Spelled ea

sea	beach	bean
teach	meals	eat
meat	peas	peaches
cream	read	neat
tea		

High-Frequency Words

a	to	friends
the	so	many
about	pushes	grows
together	of	good-bye

Bill Tried

Written by Julia Parrish

Bill and his wife
cleaned Bill's shed.
What will Bill do
with his old things?

"We can give them away,"
said Bill.
"Our friends can take
all these things."

Fred rode by.
Fred spied Bill's funny fly.
"It still flies!" cried Fred.
Bill put Fred's fly on his cart.

51

Ann came.
Ann liked Bill's big rug.
She tried to jam it in her car.
Bill put Ann's rug by the fly.

Then Lee stopped.
Lee tried to lift Bill's trunk.
The trunk is as big as Lee!

Bill put the trunk on his cart.
Bill pushed the cart to each home.

54

Then Bill went home.
What will he put
in his shed now?

Endings (Change *y* to *i*)

spied	flies
cried	tried

High-Frequency Words

what	do
old	give
away	said
our	put
to	the
pushed	now

A Day at the Park

Written by Anita Flores

Decodable
Book
111

Jean and Tom went to this park.
This park seemed nice.
At the gate it said,
"Keep this park neat."

"We will treat it well
so that we can enjoy it again,"
Tom said.

"Look at these trees!"
Jean cried.
These reds and yellows are
a nice treat."

Tom asked Jean,
"Can we play with that team?"
They played three games.

Then Tom sketched on his art pad.
Jean tried to sketch a dried leaf.
She made it look nice.

At the lake, Jean and Tom
got to feed the ducks
and see big fish.

At last this fun day ended.
"Such a nice day!" Jean cried.
"It seemed like a dream."

Endings (Change *y* to *i*)

cried
tried
dried

High-Frequency Words

to	the
said	enjoy
again	look
yellows	a
they	three

Sloan's Goal

Written by Wallace Novak

Sloan and Snow floated boats
in the pond.
Snow got soaked.

A ball came by.
"May I play?" Sloan asked.
"You're not grown up enough,"
Dave claimed.

"I'm the coach," called Joan.
"Can you kick?"
Sloan showed her his best kick.
Joan said. "Play back here."

Sloan roamed back and forth.
The wind was blowing.
The grass was growing.
Snow moaned and groaned.

Just when Sloan was going,
the ball came at him. Whoa!
Sloan kicked it.

His kick was low and not slow.
Sloan pumped his arm. Yes!
The ball had flown into the goal.

"A goal!" yelled Dave.
"You don't need to grow!"
"I'll score two in a row,"
Sloan crowed.

Long *o* Spelled *oa*

Sloan	floated	boats
soaked	coach	Joan
roamed	moaned	groaned
whoa	goal	

Long *o* Spelled *ow*

Snow	grown	showed
blowing	growing	low
slow	flown	grow
row	crowed	

High-Frequency Words

the	a	enough
you	here	said
was	into	don't
to	two	

Joan's Boat

Written by M.J. Tsou

Joan has her own boat.
Her sail has many colors.

73

Five goats got on Joan's boat.
"Where can I take you?"
asked Joan.

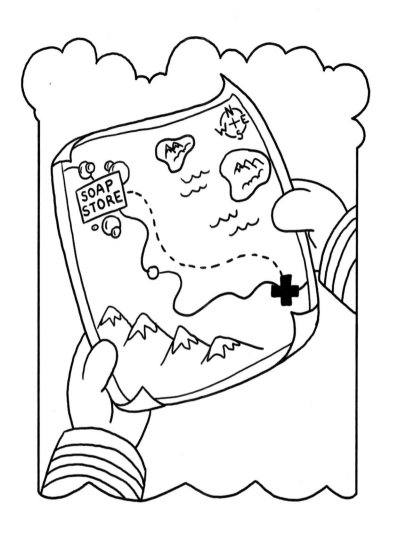

The first goat gave Joan a map.
"Please show us that soap store,"
said the goat.

"Oh, no!" cried one goat.
"Can you see that hole?"
"Grab that pail!" yelled Joan.
"I hope this boat will still float!"

Joan and the goats will save the boat.
But then the wind did not blow.
"Do not moan, Joan," said those
nice goats. "Show us how to row."

The goats helped,
but Joan's boat was slow.
Then Joan saw a fast boat.

"Will you tow my boat?"
asked Joan.
Joan and the goats went home.

Long *o* Spelled *oa*

Joan	boat	goat(s)
Joan's	soap	float
moan		

Long *o* Spelled *ow*

own	show	blow
row	slow	tow

High-Frequency Words

many	colors	where
you	the	a
said	oh	one
do	how	to
was	saw	

Scram!

Written by Dante Pelayo

Decodable
Book
114

Nell set up her tent.
She set her tent by a stream.
She made hot toast.

As she rested, Nell saw
a thing in the shrubs.
Then she saw it again.

It had stripes on its tail
and a dark mask.
It was as big as a cat.
Nell was not afraid.

She got a big, strong string.
She went to the stream
with the string.

"I will wait for that thing," Nell said.
"It will splash in this stream
and trip on my string."

Nell was brave.
She did not scream.
That thing tripped on Nell's string.
"Scram!" yelled Nell.

86

The thing ran fast.
It did not stop.
Then Nell felt safe at camp.

Three-Letter Blends

stream	shrubs	stripes
strong	string	splash
scream	scram	

High-Frequency Words

a	saw	the
again	was	afraid
to	said	

Wait for Spring

Written by Renée McLean

Toad saw a scrap.
It was a map.
He made a plan.
"I must see Bird now!" he cried.

Toad sprang up.
He packed his pillow
and a hot loaf.

He sprinted to Bird's home.
"Bird!" he yelled.
"Can you read this map?"

"We must row in that boat.
We must follow this map.
We will be rich!"

"But, Toad," said Bird,
"I have jobs at home.
And snow may come soon."

Toad did not like snow.
"That is smart," said Toad.
"We will wait for spring."

Toad stuck the map
in his coat.
He went down the road
to his snug home.

Three-Letter Blends

scrap	sprang
sprinted	spring

High-Frequency Words

saw	a
was	now
to	you
said	have
come	soon
the	down

Dwight's Flight

Written by Tina Herrera

Decodable Book 116

Dwight makes a bright red kite.
It lies on his desk while
the paint dries.

Dwight ties ten feet of cord
on the kite.
He ties the cord tight.

"May I fly my kite?" asks Dwight.
Mom tells him, "It's night.
Wait for day."

The wind is too light.
The kite lies on the grass.
Dwight tries to help it fly.

The wind starts to blow.
All right! The kite flies.
It fights to get high.
"Keep flying!" Dwight cries.

Dwight's kite looks small
in the clear skies.
Why, it might fly right
out of sight!

Then the wind dies.
The kite floats back to Dwight.
He sighs, "What a flight!"

Long *i* Spelled *ie*, *igh*

Dwight	bright	lies
dries	ties	tight
night	light	tries
right	flies	flight(s)
high	cries	skies
might	sight	dies
sighs		

High-Frequency Words

a	the	of
too	to	looks
out	what	

Just Right!

Written by Lynnette Rogers

Let's play hide and seek.
Let me look for you.
Hide out of sight!

Try to hide in this box.
The lid will not close.
It is a tight fit.

106

Try to lie under that rug.
No, it is not big!
You are not out of sight!

Can you hide in this tree?
Sit on that branch.
No, it is too high.

Inside this cave might be fine.
No, there is no light.
It is dark like night!

By this shelf might be fine.
No, I can see you in the light!
Get out of sight!

Under this bed might be fine.
I will not see you.
Yes, this is just right!

Long *i* Spelled *ie, igh*

sight	tight	lie
high	might	light
night	right	

High-Frequency Words

look	you	out
of	to	the
a	too	there

Knots for Your Wrist

Written by Ben Hollis

Decodable
Book
118

Cam's class has
Arts and Crafts Day.
The kids bring things they made
to show the class.

Kay made a wreath with her mom
to hang on her wall.
Her wreath is nice.
It smells sweet.

Len uses string for your wrist.
He ties many knots.
He gave a short strand
to each kid in class.

Jill baked muffins.
She baked with her dad.
Her dad has a knife to
cut the muffins.

116

Jane wrote a skit.
She shows her skit
while the class looks on.
Her skit is funny.

Don painted a ship.
His art looks real.
Don's mom put
it in a frame.

118

What did Cam bring?
Cam knows how to knit!
He has a bright
scarf that he made.

/n/ Spelled *kn*

knots   knife

knows   knit

/r/ Spelled *wr*

wreath   wrist

wrote

High-Frequency Words

the   they

to   a

your   many

looks   put

what

Barb Knows!

Written by Kiran Smedley

Decodable
Book
119

"I will make my pie,"
said Barb.
She wrote her list
of things to use.

Barb got fresh peaches.
She cut the peaches
with her sharp knife.

"Bring me nice plums,"
called Barb.
"I will add them
to my pie."

We gave plums
for Barb's pie.
Barb's pie got bigger.

Barb knows how to
make her pie big.
She piles more peaches and plums
on top of her pie.

Barb's pie was high.
"It's not quite as high as the sky yet,"
Barb said with a smile.

Barb put nuts right on top.
"That is how I like my pie,"
Barb said.

/n/ Spelled *kn*

knife   knows

/r/ Spelled *wr*

wrote

High-Frequency Words

said	of	to
the	how	was

Seaside Daydreams

Written by Joel Dorsch

Decodable
Book
120

Five kids and a mom are spending
a happy day at the seashore.
At lunchtime they rest in the shade
and daydream.

129

Carl dreams, "I'm pitching
in a baseball game.
My teammates and I are winning
10–0!"

Eve dreams, "I'm flying
in my own homemade plane.
It skims above the treetops."

Rick dreams, "I'm backstage
waiting for my turn to go on.
It's showtime!"

Libby dreams, "I'm drifting
on a sailboat.
I can see starfish and stingrays!"

Ray dreams, "I'm on a spaceship
going to Mars.
I hope I don't get homesick!"

At sunset Mom tells the kids,
"It's time to go home."
But the kids will keep
their seaside daydreams.

Compound Words

seashore	lunchtime	daydream(s)
baseball	teammates	homemade
treetops	backstage	showtime
sailboat	starfish	stingrays
spaceship	homesick	sunset
seaside		

High-Frequency Words

a	are	the
they	to	above
their		

Decodable Book 121

Kickball, Baseball, and Homework

Written by Lily Yeo

Liz is glad to be at school.
She has so much to do!

First Liz will play kickball.
When the bell rings,
she will go inside.

Liz will put her backpack
by her desk.
She will write to her penpal.

At lunchtime, Liz will
eat with her friends.
She has a lunchbox
just like Jen's lunchbox!

Liz and Jen play baseball
when lunch is over.
Jen races home.
Liz's team wins.

Then it is time for math.
Liz likes math.
Liz can do her homework now.

Liz will brainstorm an act
for the school play.
The big show is next week.
Liz hopes it will be funny.

Compound Words

kickball	inside	backpack
penpal	lunchtime	lunchbox
baseball	homework	brainstorm

High-Frequency Words

to	school	do
the	put	friends
a	over	now

Clues for Sue

Written by Jacob Payton

Decodable Book 122

Dad has a game for Sue.
Sue must find a few clues.

Dad helps Sue with her first clue.
"The first clue is by that fruit,"
said Dad.
"It is in that bright blue pot."

146

Sue reads her first clue.
"Take eight steps to Dad's desk.
Touch the pad to see the next clue."

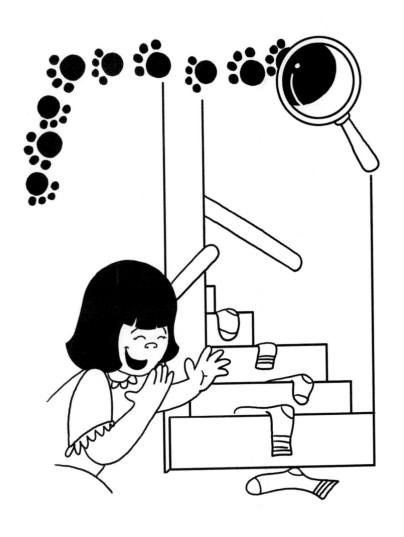

Sue reads her new clue.
"Look for the trail up the steps."
Sue runs to the steps.

She laughs.
The trail is made of Dad's socks.
Sue spots the clue by Dad's bed.
"Find Dad's new blue suit."

Sue reads her last clue.
"He likes to bark, run,
and chew."

Dad hugged Sue.
"I knew this pup
was right for Sue."

Long *oo* Spelled *ue, ew, ui*

Sue	few
clue(s)	fruit
new	blue
suit	chew
knew	

High-Frequency Words

a	find
the	said
to	touch
look	laughs
of	was

The Blue Crew

Written by Wes Long

This is a big baseball game
for the Blue Crew.
Will the team be the champs?

It is Zack's last turn at bat.
He swings. He misses.
He swings again. He misses.

Will Zack get a hit?
Will Zack cruise the bases?
He grips his bat.
Zack swings hard. Crack!

Dads and moms jump up.
Where did that ball go?

That ball is not
inside the ballpark.
That ball flew
above tall trees.

That is Zack's first hit!
The Blue Crew wins.
They are the champs!

Zack stops at the newsstand
the next day.
His snapshot is in the paper.
Zack is a baseball star!

Word Lists

Long *oo* Spelled *ew, ue, ui*

Blue	Crew	cruise
flew	newsstand	

High-Frequency Words

a	the	again
where	above	paper

160

Helpful Advice

Written by Laura Zuccari

Prue sighed deeply.
"What can I do?"
Mom was helpful.
"Take a class," she said.

Prue tried an art class.
Her paintings were frightful.
Clearly, art was not for Prue.

Prue tried an acting class.
When she got on stage,
she felt fearful.
Plainly, acting was not for Prue.

Prue tried to ride a horse.
The horse ran wildly, and
the ride was painful.
Sadly, horses were not for Prue.

164

Mom wisely chose Prue's next class.
Would Prue like it?
Mom and Prue felt hopeful.

Coach Beal showed Prue a dive.
Prue's dive was graceful.
It hardly made a splash.
Prue wanted to do more dives.

Hurray! Dives were for Prue.
Prue and Mom felt grateful.

Word Lists

Suffixes -ly, -ful

deeply	helpful	frightful
clearly	fearful	plainly
wildly	painful	sadly
wisely	hopeful	graceful
hardly	grateful	

High-Frequency Words

what	do	was
a	said	were
to	the	would
wanted		

Helpful Holly

Written by Janice Kang

Decodable Book 125

Meet Holly.
Holly is a helpful girl.
She tries to help
all the time.

Holly gladly helps
her mom get bags
from the car.

Holly helps her dad
make lunch.
She sweetly feeds
little Pete.

When her playful pup
got in thick mud,
Holly quickly gave Sam
a nice bath.

Holly helps in her class.
She keeps the room clean.
She picks up paper.
She is nice and speaks softly.

Holly helps her friends too.
Jen did not walk slowly.
When she fell,
Holly helped her up.

Holly is helpful at home.
Holly is helpful at school.
You can be helpful too!
How can you help?

Word Lists

Suffixes *-ly, -ful*

helpful	gladly	sweetly
playful	quickly	softly
slowly		

High-Frequency Words

a	to	the
little	paper	friends
school	you	too
how		

Zoom! Zoom!

Written by Rob Stern

Luke is fast.
He walks so fast
that he misses
many things.

Luke went to the zoo.
Luke went quickly past apes.
Other kids stopped.
Luke zoomed on.

Luke sped past snakes.
They were huge!
Other kids stayed to look.
Luke zoomed on.

Luke zipped past birds.
"Coo, coo," called bright birds.
Luke did not stop.
He zoomed on.

At noon a man
gave food to the fish.
Fish swim fast for food!
Luke zoomed on.

Seals threw balls in hoops.
All the kids thought it was fun.
Luke missed the show.

"What did you see at the zoo?"
Mom asked.
"I do not remember!" cried Luke.
"It all went by too fast!"

Long *oo* Spelled *oo*

zoo	zoomed	coo
noon	food	hoops
too		

High-Frequency Words

many	to	the
other	they	were
thought	was	what
you	do	remember

To the Moon

Written by Reonne Reed

Kim and Dan made a plan.
They will go up to the Moon!

"Can we get there?" Kim asked.
"We will need a big spaceship."

Dan quickly got tools.
"Use those tools safely,"
he said.

When they made the ship,
Kim got food for them.
"Is this all we need?" she asked.

"We need water too," Dan said.
He filled his jug.
He got a jug for Kim too.

Kim and Dan got in.
It had lots of room.
Dan was hopeful.

The big spaceship did not start.
"Oh, well," Dan said sadly.
"We can try again."

Word Lists

Long *oo* Spelled *oo*

moon	tools	food
too	room	

High-Frequency Words

a	they	to
the	there	said
water	oh	again